COLOUR MY CLASSICS
WILLIAM SHAKESPEARE

Troilus and Cresside, Act 4, scene 2

COLOUR MY CLASSICS

WILLIAM SHAKESPEARE

Includes 40 evocative drawings with matching text

WORTH PRESS

Colour My Classics: William Shakespeare first published in 2016
by Worth Press Limited, Cambridge
UK www.worthpress.co.uk

Concept, text, illustrations, text and illustrations selection,
design and production specification
copyright © Worth Press Limited 2016

ISBN 978 1 84931 122 9

Printed in China by Imago

Contents

Introduction to
Colour My Classics:
William Shakespeare

To all adults who remember the pleasure they derived from 'colouring in' when they were children this book offers a unique way to rediscover that pleasure and at the same time to acquire a whole new perspective on the immortal bard and his universally celebrated plays. Colouring is very therapeutic: it relaxes the brainwaves, calming the mind and smoothing away the anxieties and pressures of the day as you concentrate your attention on this most rewarding activity. So enjoy this creative way to explore the dramatic landscape imagined by Shakespeare, for whom all the world was a stage and all the men and women players.

William Shakespeare's World

Born some four hundred years ago, the talented young playwright who grew up in Elizabeth I's Merrie England is today the most read wordsmith in the world, drawing enthusiastic admiration from every age group, every nation and every category of audience. In Shakespeare's day, when he was numbered among the actors on the stage, plays were performed to boisterous audiences that included the groundlings, who paid just one penny to stand right in front of the stage. A line in his play *Henry VIII* describes 'the youths that thunder at a playhouse, and fight for bitten apples'. This potential rabble included hecklers as well as loud, enthusiastic participants, shoving, manoeuvring and undoubtedly making eyes at the opposite sex as well as urging on the players and cheering the antics of the back-stage crew. Meanwhile, the richer patrons relaxed in the covered galleries, paying as much as half a crown each for their coveted seats. At the most prestigious end of the scale, the dramas were also presented at the courts of both Queen Elizabeth I and King James I.

To be successful, plays had to appeal to this wide sweep of spectators – and Shakespeare's still do today. He is among the most translated authors in history, and the sales of his works are eclipsed only by those of the Bible. As Ben Jonson observed: 'He was not of an age, but for all time!' This most popular dramatist and poet certainly told every kind of story. His comedies, tragedies and histories encompass all genres and topics – melodrama, fairy tales, adventure, horror, love stories, humour, burlesque, death, politics, war and romance. The stories transcend time and culture and are as powerful today as ever they were in the 1500s. Their appeal is universal but at the same time personal, pertinent to every individual watching.

Full of twists of fate that add to the drama of the climactic plots, the stories often incorporate magic and superstition, spells, fairies, witches and ghosts. They were penned at a time when witchcraft was taken very seriously; King James himself wrote a book about witches and demons. In sixteenth-century Europe, alchemists were still trying to transform base metals into gold, people believed the stars and planets controlled their lives and Elizabeth I's astronomer, Dr John Dee, was researching the language of the angels.

Most of the plays were based upon existing stories, *A Midsummer Night's Dream*, *Love's Labour's Lost* and *The Tempest*, are entirely original. Shakespeare unashamedly borrowed many of his plots and was inspired by stories from the Bible as well as the works of other writers. He was not among those geniuses overlooked in his time, but was very much appreciated and of great renown while alive.

It is hoped that the illustrations of his works presented here for you to enhance manage in some way to encapsulate the glory of this amazing man and the richness of his legacy.

Midsummer's Night Dream

PUCK   How now, spirit! Whither wander you?

FAIRY   Over hill, over dale,

        Thorough bush, thorough briar,

        Over park, over pale,

        Thorough flood, thorough fire,

        I do wander everywhere,

        Swifter than the moon's sphere:

        And I serve the Fairy Queen,

        To dew her orbs upon the green.

        The cowslips tall her pensioners be,

        In their gold coats spots you see:

        Those be rubies, fairy favours:

        In those freckles live their savours.

        I must go seek some dewdrops here,

        And hang a pearl in every cowslip's ear.

        Farewell, thou lob of spirits: I'll be gone –

        Our queen and all her elves come here anon.

ACT 2, SCENE 1

Romeo and Juliet

JULIET   It is, it is! Hie hence, be gone, away!

It is the lark that sings so out of tune,

Straining harsh discords and unpleasing sharps.

Some say the lark makes sweet division:

This doth not so, for she divideth us.

Some say the lark and loathèd toad changed eyes;

O now I would they had changed voices too,

Since arm from arm that voice doth us affray,

Hunting thee hence with hunt's-up to the day.

O now be gone! More light and light it grows.

ROMEO   More light and light, more dark and dark our woes.

NURSE   Madam!

JULIET   Nurse?

NURSE   Your lady mother is coming to your chamber.

The day is broke; be wary, look about.

JULIET   Then, window, let day in and let life out.

ROMEO   Farewell, farewell; one kiss, and I'll descend.

ACT 3, SCENE 5

Hamlet

HAMLET   Let me see. [*he takes the skull*] Alas, poor Yorick! I knew him, Horatio – a fellow of infinite jest, of most excellent fancy. He hath borne me on his back a thousand times, and now how abhorred in my imagination it is! My gorge rises at it. Here hung those lips that I have kissed I know not how oft. Where be your gibes now? Your gambols, your songs, your flashes of merriment, that were wont to set the table on a roar? Not one now to mock your own grinning? Quite chop fallen? Now get you to my lady's chamber, and tell her, let her paint an inch thick, to this favour she must come. Make her laugh at that. Prithee, Horatio, tell me one thing.

ACT 5, SCENE 1

As You Like It

TOUCHSTONE	He, sir, that must marry this woman. Therefore, you clown, abandon (which is in the vulgar 'leave') the society (which in the boorish is 'company') of this female (which in the common is 'woman'); which together is, 'abandon the society of this female,' or, clown, thou perishest; or, to thy better understanding, diest; or, to wit, I kill thee, make thee away, translate thy life into death, thy liberty into bondage: I will deal in poison with thee, or in bastinado, or in steel; I will bandy with thee in faction; I will o'er-run thee with policy; I will kill thee a hundred and fifty ways – therefore tremble and depart.
AUDREY	Do, good William.
WILLIAM	God rest you merry, sir.

ACT 5, SCENE 1

The Two Gentlemen of Verona

JULIA   Counsel, Lucetta; gentle girl, assist me;
And, ev'n in kind love, I do conjure thee,
Who art the table wherein all my thoughts
Are visibly character'd and engrav'd,
To lesson me and tell me some good mean
How, with my honour, I may undertake
A journey to my loving Proteus.

LUCETTA   Alas, the way is wearisome and long!

JULIA   A true-devoted pilgrim is not weary
To measure kingdoms with his feeble steps;
Much less shall she that hath Love's wings to fly,
And when the flight is made to one so dear,
Of such divine perfection, as Sir Proteus.

ACT 1, SECENE 7

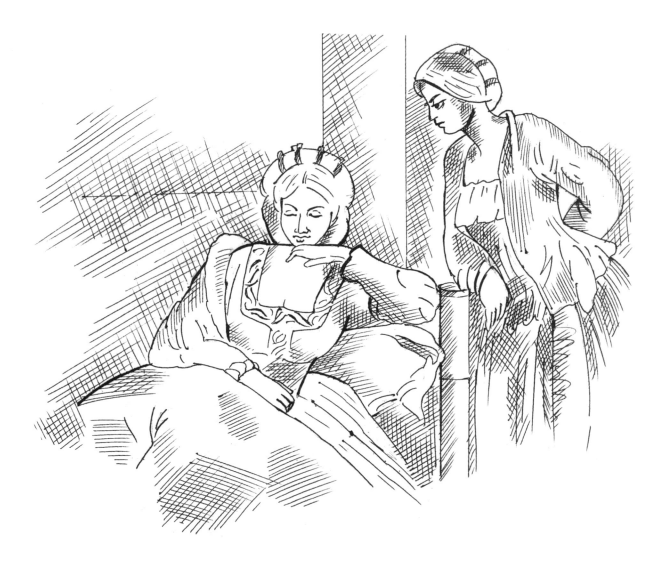

Love's Labour's Lost

MOTH   'All hail, the richest beauties on the earth!'

BOYET   Beauties no richer than rich taffeta. [*Aside*

MOTH   A holy parcel of the fairest dames

        [*The ladies turn their bcks to him!*

        That ever turn'd their – backs – to mortal views!

ACT 5, SCENE 2

18

Romeo and Juliet

ROMEO   Draw, Benvolio; beat down their weapons.

Gentlemen, for shame! forbear this outrage!

Tybalt, Mercutio, the Prince expressly hath

Forbid this bandying in Verona streets.

Hold, Tybalt! Good Mercutio!

> *[Tybalt under Romeo's arm thrusts Mercutio in,*
> *and flies with his followers*

MERCUTIO   I am hurt.

A plague o' both your houses! I am sped.

Is he gone and hath nothing?

BENVOLIO   What, art thou hurt?

MERCUTIO   Ay, ay, a scratch, a scratch. Marry, 'tis enough.

Where is my page? Go, villain, fetch a surgeon.

> *[Exit page*

ACT3, SCENE 1

King Lear

EDGAR　　As I stood here below, methought his eyes

　　　　　Were two full moons; he had a thousand noses,

　　　　　Horns whelk'd and wav'd like the enridged sea.

　　　　　It was some fiend. Therefore, thou happy father,

　　　　　Think that the clearest gods, who make them honours

　　　　　Of men's impossibility, have preserv'd thee.

GLOUCESTER　I do remember now. Henceforth I'll bear

　　　　　Affliction till it do cry out itself

　　　　　'Enough, enough,' and die. That thing you speak of,

　　　　　I took it for a man. Often 'twould say

　　　　　'The fiend, the fiend'- he led me to that place.

EDGAR　　Bear free and patient thoughts.

Enter Lear, mad,

fantastically dressed with weeds

　　　　　But who comes here?

　　　　　The safer sense will ne'er accommodate

　　　　　His master thus.

LEAR　　　No, they cannot touch me for coming;

　　　　　I am the King himself.

King Lear

EDMUND Know of the Duke if his last purpose hold,
Or whether since he is advis'd by aught
To change the course. He's full of alteration
And self-reproving. Bring his constant pleasure.

[Exit an officer

REGAN Our sister's man is certainly miscarried.

EDMUND Tis to be doubted, madam.

REGAN   Now, sweet lord,
You know the goodness I intend upon you.
Tell me – but truly – but then speak the truth –
Do you not love my sister?

EDMUND   In honour'd love.

REGAN But have you never found my brother's way
To the forfended place?

EDMUND   That thought abuses you.

REGAN I am doubtful that you have been conjunct
And bosom'd with her, as far as we call hers.

EDMUND No, by mine honour, madam.

REGAN I never shall endure her. Dear my lord,
Be not familiar with her.

EDMUND   Fear me not.
She and the Duke her husband!

ACT 5, SCENE 1

King Richard III

GLOUCESTER   Now is the winter of our discontent
Made glorious summer by this sun of York;
And all the clouds that lour'd upon our house
In the deep bosom of the ocean buried.
Now are our brows bound with victorious wreaths;
Our bruised arms hung up for monuments;
Our stern alarums chang'd to merry meetings,
Our dreadful marches to delightful measures.
Grim-visag'd war hath smooth'd his wrinkled front,
And now, instead of mounting barbed steeds
To fright the souls of fearful adversaries,
He capers nimbly in a lady's chamber
To the lascivious pleasing of a lute.
But I – that am not shap'd for sportive tricks,
Nor made to court an amorous looking-glass;
I – that am rudely stamp'd, and want love's majesty
To strut before a wanton ambling nymph;
I – that am curtail'd of this fair proportion,
Cheated of feature by dissembling nature,
Deform'd, unfinish'd, sent before my time
Into this breathing world scarce half made up,
And that so lamely and unfashionable
That dogs bark at me as I halt by them –
Why, I, in this weak piping time of peace,
Have no delight to pass away the time,
Unless to spy my shadow in the sun
And descant on mine own deformity.
About a prophecy which says that G
Of Edward's heirs the murderer shall be.
Dive, thoughts, down to my soul. Here Clarence comes.

ACT 1, SCENE 1

Othello

OTHELLO It is the cause, it is the cause, my soul.

Let me not name it to you, you chaste stars!

It is the cause. Yet I'll not shed her blood,

Nor scar that whiter skin of hers than snow

And smooth as monumental alabaster.

Yet she must die, else she'll betray more men.

Put out the light, and then put out the light.

I can again thy former light restore,

Should I repent me; but once put out thy light,

Thou cunning'st pattern of excelling nature,

I know not where is that Promethean heat

That can thy light relume. When I have pluck'd the rose,

 I cannot give it vital growth again,

It must needs wither; I'll smell it on the tree. [*Kisses her*

ACT 5, SCENE 2

Antony and Cleopatra

ANTONY Let Rome in Tiber melt, and the wide arch

Of the rang'd empire fall! Here is my space.

Kingdoms are clay; our dungy earth alike

Feeds beast as man. The nobleness of life

Is to do thus [emhracing], when such a mutual pair

And such a twain can do't, in which I bind,

On pain of punishment, the world to weet

We stand up peerless.

CLEOPATRA Excellent falsehood!

Why did he marry Fulvia, and not love her?

I'll seem the fool I am not. Antony

Will be himself.

ANTONY But stirr'd by Cleopatra.

Now for the love of Love and her soft hours,

Let's not confound the time with conference harsh;

There's not a minute of our lives should stretch

Without some pleasure now. What sport tonight?

ACT 1, SCENE 1

King Henry IV

FALSTAFF   By the mass, lad, thou sayest true; it is like we shall have good trading that way. But tell me, Hal, art not thou horrible afeard? Thou being heir apparent, could the world pick thee out three such enemies again as that fiend Douglas, that spirit Percy, and that devil Glendower? Art thou not horribly afraid? Doth not thy blood thrill at it?

PRINCE   Not a whit, i' faith. I lack some of thy instinct.

FALSTAFF   Well, thou wilt be horribly chid to-morrow when thou comest to thy father. If thou love me, practise an answer.

PRINCE   Do thou stand for my father and examine me upon the particulars of my life.

FALSTAFF   Shall I? Content. This chair shall be my state, this dagger my sceptre, and this cushion my, crown.

PRINCE   Thy state is taken for a join'd-stool, thy golden sceptre for a leaden dagger, and thy precious rich crown for a pitiful bald crown.

FALSTAFF   Well, an the fire of grace be not quite out of thee, now shalt thou be moved. Give me a cup of sack to make my eyes look red, that it may be thought I have wept; for I must speak in passion, and I will do it in King Cambyses' vein.

PRINCE   Well, here is my leg.

FALSTAFF   And here is my speech. Stand aside, nobility.

HOSTESS   O Jesu, this is excellent sport, i' faith!

FALSTAFF   Weep not, sweet queen, for trickling tears are vain.

HOSTESS   O, the Father, how he holds his countenance!

FALSTAFF   For God's sake, lords, convey my tristful queen!
For tears do stop the floodgates of her eyes.

HOSTESS   O Jesu, he doth it as like one of these harlotry players as ever I see!

ACT 2, SCENE 4

King Henry IV

PRINCE   It will not be accepted, on my life.

The Douglas and the Hotspur both together

Are confident against the world in arms.

KING   Hence, therefore, every leader to his charge;

For, on their answer, will we set on them,

And God befriend us as our cause is just!

Exeunt King, Blunt and Prince John

FALSTAFF   Hal, if thou see me down in the battle and bestride me, so! 'Tis a point of friendship.

PRINCE   Nothing but a Colossus can do thee that friendship. Say thy prayers, and farewell.

FALSTAFF   I would 'twere bedtime, Hal, and all well.

PRINCE   Why, thou owest God a death. *Exit*

FALSTAFF   'Tis not due yet. I would be loath to pay him before his day. What need I be so forward with him that calls not on me? Well, 'tis no matter; honour pricks me on. Yea, but how if honour prick me off when I come on? How then? Can honor set to a leg? No. Or an arm? No. Or take away the grief of a wound? No. Honour hath no skill in surgery then? No. What is honour? A word. What is that word honour? Air. A trim reckoning! Who hath it? He that died a Wednesday. Doth he feel it? No. Doth be bear it? No. 'Tis insensible then? Yea, to the dead. But will it not live with the living? No. Why? Detraction will not suffer it. Therefore I'll none of it. Honour is a mere scutcheon- and so ends my catechism.

ACT 5, SCENE 1

Hamlet

HAMLET So you mis-take your husbands – Begin, murderer. Pox! Leave thy damnable faces and begin! Come – 'the croaking raven doth bellow for revenge.'

LUCIANUA Thoughts black, hands apt, drugs fit, and time agreeing,
Confederate season, else no creature seeing,
Thou mixture rank, of midnight weeds collected,
With Hecate's ban thrice blasted, thrice infected,
Thy natural magic and dire property
On wholesome life usurps immediately.

[*He pours the poison into the sleeper's ears.*

HAMLET He poisons him i'th'garden for's estate. His name's Gonzago: the story is extant, and written in very choice Italian. You shall see anon how the murderer gets the love of Gonzago's wife.

OPHELIA The King rises.

HAMLET What, frighted with false fire?

QUEEN How fares my lord?

POLONIUS Give o'er the play.

KING Give me some light – away!

POLONIUS Lights, lights, lights!

ACT 3, SCENE 2

Hamlet

OPHELIA   There's rosemary, that's for remembrance. Pray you, love, remember. And there is pansies, that's for thoughts.

LAERTES   A document in madness! Thoughts and remembrance fitted.

OPHELIA   There's fennel for you, and columbines. There's rue for you, and here's some for me. We may call it herb of grace o' Sundays. O, you must wear your rue with a difference! There's a daisy. I would give you some violets, but they wither'd all when my father died. They say he made a good end.

ACT 4, SCENE 5

King Henry VIII

WOLSEY   I am glad
Your Grace is grown so pleasant.

KING   My Lord Chamberlain,
Prithee come hither: what fair lady's that?

CHAMBERLAIN   An't please your Grace, Sir Thomas Bullen's daughter-
The Viscount Rochford-one of her Highness' women.

KING   By heaven, she is a dainty one. Sweet heart,
I were unmannerly to take you out
And not to kiss you. A health, gentlemen!
Let it go round.

WOLSEY   Sir Thomas Lovell, is the banquet ready
I' th' privy chamber?

LOVELL   Yes, my lord.

WOLSEY   Your Grace,
I fear, with dancing is a little heated.

KING   I fear, too much.

WOLSEY   There's fresher air, my lord,
In the next chamber.

KING   Lead in your ladies, ev'ry one. Sweet partner,
I must not yet forsake you. Let's be merry:
Good my Lord Cardinal, I have half a dozen healths
To drink to these fair ladies, and a measure
To lead 'em once again; and then let's dream
Who's best in favour. Let the music knock it.

[Exeunt, with trumpets

ACT 1, SCENE 4

Troilus and Cressida

TROILUS	Dear, trouble not yourself; the morn is cold.
CRESSIDA	Then, sweet my lord, I'll call mine uncle down;
	He shall unbolt the gates.
TROILUS	Trouble him not;
	To bed, to bed! Sleep kill those pretty eyes,
	And give as soft attachment to thy senses
	As infants' empty of all thought!
CRESSIDA	Good morrow, then.
TROILUS	I prithee now, to bed.
CRESSIDA	Are you aweary of me?
TROILUS	O Cressida! but that the busy day,
	Wak'd by the lark, hath rous'd the ribald crows,
	And dreaming night will hide our joys no longer,
	I would not from thee.
CRESSIDA	Night hath been too brief.
TROILUS	Beshrew the witch! with venomous wights she stays
	As tediously as hell, but flies the grasps of love
	With wings more momentary-swift than thought.
	You will catch cold, and curse me.
CRESSIDA	Prithee tarry.
	You men will never tarry.
	O foolish Cressid! I might have still held off,
	And then you would have tarried. Hark! there's one up.

ACT 4, SCENE 2

Macbeth

LADY MACBETH	Who was it that thus cried? Why, worthy Thane,
	You do unbend your noble strength, to think
	So brainsickly of things. Go, get some water
	And wash this filthy witness from your hand.
	Why did you bring these daggers from the place?
	They must lie there. Go carry them, and smear
	The sleepy grooms with blood.
MACBETH	I'll go no more.
	I am afraid to think what I have done;
	Look on't again I dare not.
LADY MACBETH	Infirm of purpose!
	Give me the daggers. The sleeping and the dead
	Are but as pictures; 'tis the eye of childhood
	That fears a painted devil. If he do bleed,
	I'll gild the faces of the grooms withal,
	For it must seem their guilt. [*Exit. Knocking within*
MACBETH	Whence is that knocking?
	How is't with me, when every noise appals me?
	What hands are here? Ha, they pluck out mine eyes!
	Will all great Neptune's ocean wash this blood
	Clean from my hand? No, this my hand will rather
	The multitudinous seas incarnadine,
	Making the green one red.

ACT 2, SCENE1

The Two Gentlemen of Verona

VALENTINE   Cease to persuade, my loving Proteus:

Home-keeping youth have ever homely wits.

Were't not affection chains thy tender days

To the sweet glances of thy honour'd love,

I rather would entreat thy company

To see the wonders of the world abroad,

Than, living dully sluggardis'd at home,

Wear out thy youth with shapeless idleness.

But since thou lov'st, love still, and thrive therein,

Even as I would, when I to love begin.

PROTEUS   Wilt thou be gone? Sweet Valentine, adieu!

Think on thy Proteus, when thou haply seest

Some rare noteworthy object in thy travel.

Wish me partaker in thy happiness

When thou dost meet good hap; and in thy danger,

If ever danger do environ thee,

Commend thy grievance to my holy prayers,

For I will be thy headsman, Valentine.

ACT 1, SCENE 1

The Comedy of Errors

SECOND MERCHANT	Well, officer, arrest him at my suit.
OFFICER	I do; and charge you in the Duke's name to obey me.
ANGELO	This touches me in reputation.
	Either consent to pay this sum for me,
	Or I attach you by this officer.
ANTIPHOLUS OF EPHASUS	Consent to pay thee that I never had!
	Arrest me, foolish fellow, if thou dar'st.
ANGELO	Here is thy fee; arrest him, officer.
	I would not spare my brother in this case,
	If he should scorn me so apparently.
OFFICER	I do arrest you, sir; you hear the suit.
ANTIPHOLUS OF EPHASUS	I do obey thee till I give thee bail.
	But, sirrah, you shall buy this sport as dear
	As all the metal in your shop will answer.
ANGELO	Sir, sir, I shall have law in Ephesus,
	To your notorious shame, I doubt it not.

Enter Dromio of Syracuse, from the bay

DROMIO OF SYRACUSE	Master, there's a bark of Epida

ACT 4, SCENE 1

A Midsummer Night's Dream

THESEUS   Now, fair Hippolyta, our nuptial hour
           Draws on apace; four happy days bring in
           Another moon; but, O, methinks, how slow
           This old moon wanes! She lingers my desires,
           Like to a step-dame or a dowager,
           Long withering out a young man's revenue.

HIPPOLYTA Four days will quickly steep themselves in night;
           Four nights will quickly dream away the time;
           And then the moon, like to a silver bow
           New-bent in heaven, shall behold the night
           Of our solemnities.

ACT 1, SCENE 1

The Taming of the Shrew

BIANCA   In time I may believe, yet I mistrust.

LUCENTIO   Mistrust it not- for sure, AEacides

Was Ajax, call'd so from his grandfather.

BIANCA   I must believe my master; else, I promise you,

I should be arguing still upon that doubt;

But let it rest. Now, Licio, to you.

Good master, take it not unkindly, pray,

That I have been thus pleasant with you both.

HORTENSIO   [*To Lucentio*] You may go walk and give me leave awhile;

My lessons make no music in three Parts.

LUCENTIO   Are you so formal, sir? Well, I must wait,

[Aside] And watch withal; for, but I be deceiv'd,

Our fine musician groweth amorous.

HORTENSIO   Madam, before you touch the instrument

To learn the order of my fingering,

I must begin with rudiments of art,

To teach you gamut in a briefer sort,

More pleasant, pithy, and effectual,

Than hath been taught by any of my trade;

And there it is in writing fairly drawn.

ACT 3, SCENE 1

King John

CONSTANCE   You have beguil'd me with a counterfeit
Resembling majesty, which, being touch'd and tried,
Proves valueless; you are forsworn, forsworn;
You came in arms to spill mine enemies' blood,
But now in arms you strengthen it with yours.
The grappling vigour and rough frown of war
Is cold in amity and painted peace,
And our oppression hath made up this league.
Arm, arm, you heavens, against these perjur'd kings!
A widow cries: Be husband to me, heavens!
Let not the hours of this ungodly day
Wear out the day in peace; but, ere sunset,
Set armed discord 'twixt these perjur'd kings!
Hear me, O, hear me.

ACT 3, SCENE 1

King Richard II

BOLINGBROKE	Stand all apart,
	And show fair duty to his Majesty. [*He kneels down*]
	My gracious lord –
KING RICHARD	Fair cousin, you debase your princely knee
	To make the base earth proud with kissing it.
	Me rather had my heart might feel your love
	Than my unpleas'd eye see your courtesy.
	Up, cousin, up; your heart is up, I know,
	[*Touching his own head*] Thus high at least, although
	your knee below.
BOLINGBROKE	My gracious lord, I come but for mine own.
KING RICHARD	Your own is yours, and I am yours, and all.
BOLINGBROKE	So far be mine, my most redoubted lord,
	As my true service shall deserve your love.
KING RICHARD	Well you deserve. They well deserve to have
	That know the strong'st and surest way to get.
	Uncle, give me your hands; nay, dry your eyes:
	Tears show their love, but want their remedies.
	Cousin, I am too young to be your father,
	Though you are old enough to be my heir.
	What you will have, I'll give, and willing too;
	For do we must what force will have us do.
	Set on towards London. Cousin, is it so?
BOLINGBROKE	Yea, my good lord.
KING RICHARD	Then I must not say no.

[*Flourish. Exeunt*

ACT 2, SCENE 3

The Merchant of Venice

SOLANIO Now, what news on the Rialto?

SALERIO Why, yet it lives there uncheck'd that Antonio hath a ship of rich lading wreck'd on the narrow seas; the Goodwins I think they call the place, a very dangerous flat and fatal, where the carcases of many a tall ship lie buried, as they say, if my gossip Report be an honest woman of her word.

SOLANIO I would she were as lying a gossip in that as ever knapp'd ginger or made her neighbours believe she wept for the death of a third husband. But it is true, without any slips of prolixity or crossing the plain highway of talk, that the good Antonio, the honest Antonio- O that I had a title good enough to keep his name company!-

SALERIO Come, the full stop.

SOLANIO Ha! What sayest thou? Why, the end is, he hath lost a ship.

SALERIO I would it might prove the end of his losses.

ACT 3, SCENE 1

Much Ado About Nothing

LEON   I learn in this letter that Don Pedro of Arragon comes this night to Messina.

MESSENGER   He is very near by this. He was not three leagues off when I left him.

LEON   How many gentlemen have you lost in this action?

MESSENGER   But few of any sort, and none of name.

LEON   A victory is twice itself when the achiever brings home full numbers. I find here that Don Pedro hath bestowed much honour on a young Florentine called Claudio.

MESSENGER   Much deserv'd on his part, and equally rememb'red by Don

PEDRO   He hath borne himself beyond the promise of his age, doing in the figure of a lamb the feats of a lion. He hath indeed better bett'red expectation than you must expect of me to tell you how.

LEON   He hath an uncle here in Messina will be very much glad of it.

MESSENGER   I have already delivered him letters, and there appears much joy in him; even so much that joy could not show itself modest enough without a badge of bitterness.

LEON   Did he break out into tears?

MESSENGER   In great measure.

LEON   A kind overflow of kindness. There are no faces truer than those that are so wash'd. How much better is it to weep at joy than to joy at weeping!

ACT 1, SCENE 1

Measure for Measure

BOY   *[singing]*

> Take, O, take those lips away,
>
> That so sweetly were forsworn;
>
> And those eyes, the break of day,
>
> Lights that do mislead the morn;
>
> But my kisses bring again, bring again;
>
> Seals of love, but seal'd in vain, seal'd in vain.

Enter Duke, disguised as before

MARIANA   Break off thy song, and haste thee quick away;

Here comes a man of comfort, whose advice

Hath often still'd my brawling discontent.   *[Exit boy*

I cry you mercy, sir, and well could wish

You had not found me here so musical.

Let me excuse me, and believe me so,

My mirth it much displeas'd, but pleas'd my woe.

DUKE   'Tis good; though music oft hath such a charm

To make bad good and good provoke to harm.

I pray you tell me hath anybody inquir'd for me here to-day.

Much upon this time have I promis'd here to meet.

MARIANA   You have not been inquir'd after; I have sat here all day.

ACT 4, SCENE 1

Titus Andronicus

SATURNINUS   Noble patricians, patrons of my right,

Defend the justice of my cause with arms;

And, countrymen, my loving followers,

Plead my successive title with your swords.

I am his first born son that was the last

That ware the imperial diadem of Rome;

Then let my father's honours live in me,

Nor wrong mine age with this indignity.

BASSIANUS   Romans, friends, followers, favourers of my right,

If ever Bassianus, Caesar's son,

Were gracious in the eyes of royal Rome,

Keep then this passage to the Capitol;

And suffer not dishonour to approach

The imperial seat, to virtue consecrate,

To justice, continence, and nobility;

But let desert in pure election shine;

And, Romans, fight for freedom in your choice.

ACT 1, SCENE 1

The Tempest

BOATSWAIN	Down with the topmast. Yare, lower, lower! Bring her to try wi' th' maincourse. [*A cry within*] A plague upon this howling! They are louder than the weather or our office.
	Re-enter Sebastian, Antonio and Gonzalo
	Yet again! What do you here? Shall we give o'er, and drown? Have you a mind to sink?
SEBASTIAN	A pox o' your throat, you bawling, blasphemous, incharitable dog!
BOATSWAIN	Work you, then.
ANTONIO	Hang, cur; hang, you whoreson, insolent noisemaker; we are less afraid to be drown'd than thou art.
GONZALO	I'll warrant him for drowning, though the ship were no stronger than a nutshell, and as leaky as an unstanched wench.
BOATSWAIN	Lay her a-hold, a-hold; set her two courses; off to sea again; lay her off.
	Enter mariners – wet
MARINERS	All lost! to prayers, to prayers! all lost! [*Exeunt*
BOATSWAIN	What, must our mouths be cold?
GONZALO	The King and Prince at prayers! Let's assist them, For our case is as theirs.
SEBASTIAN	I am out of patience.
ANTONIO	We are merely cheated of our lives by drunkards. This wide-chopp'd rascal – would thou mightst lie drowning The washing of ten tides!
GONZALO	He'll be hang'd yet, Though every drop of water swear against it, And gape at wid'st to glut him.

ACT 1, SCENE 1

As You Like It

ROSALIND   O Jupiter, how weary are my spirits!

TOUCHSTONE   I care not for my spirits, if my legs were not weary.

ROSALIND   I could find in my heart to disgrace my man's apparel, and to cry like a woman; but I must comfort the weaker vessel, as doublet and hose ought to show itself courageous to petticoat; therefore, courage, good Aliena.

CELIA   I pray you bear with me; I cannot go no further.

TOUCHSTONE   For my part, I had rather bear with you than bear you; yet I should bear no cross if I did bear you; for I think you have no money in your purse.

ROSALIND   Well,. this is the Forest of Arden.

TOUCHSTONE   Ay, now am I in Arden; the more fool I; when I was at home I was in a better place; but travellers must be content.

ACT 2, SCENE 4

King Henry VI

QUEEN MARGARET	Welcome, my lord, to this brave town of York.
	Yonder's the head of that arch-enemy
	That sought to be encompass'd with your crown.
	Doth not the object cheer your heart, my lord?
KING HENRY	Ay, as the rocks cheer them that fear their wreck –
	To see this sight, it irks my very soul.
	Withhold revenge, dear God; 'tis not my fault,
	Nor wittingly have I infring'd my vow.
CLIFFORD	My gracious liege, this too much lenity
	And harmful pity must be laid aside.
	To whom do lions cast their gentle looks?
	Not to the beast that would usurp their den.
	Whose hand is that the forest bear doth lick?
	Not his that spoils her young before her face.
	Who scapes the lurking serpent's mortal sting?
	Not he that sets his foot upon her back,
	The smallest worm will turn, being trodden on,
	And doves will peck in safeguard of their brood.
	Ambitious York did level at thy crown,
	Thou smiling while he knit his angry brows.
	He, but a Duke, would have his son a king,
	And raise his issue like a loving sire:
	Thou, being a king, bless'd with a goodly son,
	Didst yield consent to disinherit him,
	Which argued thee a most unloving father.

ACT 2, SCENE 2

The Winter's Tale

AUTOCLYTUS	I am robb'd, sir, and beaten; my money and apparel ta'en from me, and these detestable things put upon me.
CLOWN	What, by a horseman or a footman?
AUTOCLYTUS	A footman, sweet sir, a footman.
CLOWN	Indeed, he should be a footman, by the garments he has left with thee; if this be a horseman's coat, it hath seen very hot service. Lend me thy hand, I'll help thee. Come, lend me thy hand. [*helping him up*]
AUTOCLYTUS	O, good sir, tenderly, O!
CLOWN	Alas, poor soul!
AUTOCLYTUS	O, good sir, softly, good sir; I fear, sir, my shoulder blade is out.
CLOWN	How now! Canst stand?
AUTOCLYTUS	Softly, dear sir [*picks his pocket*]; good sir, softly. You ha' done me a charitable office.
CLOWN	Dost lack any money? I have a little money for thee.
AUTOCLYTUS	No, good sweet sir; no, I beseech you, sir. I have a kinsman not past three quarters of a mile hence, unto whom I was going; I shall there have money or anything I want. Offer me no money, I pray you; that kills my heart.
CLOWN	What manner of fellow was he that robb'd you?
AUTOCLYTUS	A fellow, sir, that I have known to go about with troll-my-dames; I knew him once a servant of the Prince. I cannot tell, good sir, for which of his virtues it was, but he was certainly whipt out of the court.

ACT 4, SCENE 2

King Henry V

KING HENRY Peace to this meeting, wherefore we are met!

Unto our brother France, and to our sister,

Health and fair time of day; joy and good wishes

To our most fair and princely cousin Katherine.

And, as a branch and member of this royalty,

By whom this great assembly is contriv'd,

We do salute you, Duke of Burgundy.

And, princes French, and peers, health to you all!

FRENCH KING Right joyous are we to behold your face,

Most worthy brother England; fairly met!

So are you, princes English, every one.

QUEEN ISABEL So happy be the issue, brother England,

Of this good day and of this gracious meeting

As we are now glad to behold your eyes-

Your eyes, which hitherto have home in them,

Against the French that met them in their bent,

The fatal balls of murdering basilisks;

The venom of such looks, we fairly hope,

Have lost their quality; and that this day

Shall change all griefs and quarrels into love.

KING HENRY To cry amen to that, thus we appear.

QUEEN ISABEL You English princes an, I do salute you.

ACT 5, SCENE 2

Twelfth Night

AGUECHEEK	Now, sir, have I met you again?
	[*striking Sebastian*] There's for you.
SEBASTIAN	Why, there's for thee, and there, and there.
	Are all the people mad?
SIR TOBY	Hold, sir, or I'll throw your dagger o'er the house. [*holding Sebastain*]
CLOWN	This will I tell my lady straight. I would not be in some of our coats for two-pence. [*Exit*
SIR TOBY	Come on, sir; hold.
AGUECHEEK	Nay, let him alone. I'll go another way to work with him; I'll have an action of battery against him, if there be any law in Illyria; though I struck him first, yet it's no matter for that.
SEBASTIAN	Let go thy hand.
SIR TOBY	Come, sir, I will not let you go. Come, my young soldier, put up your iron; you are well flesh'd. Come on.
SEBASTIAN	will be free from thee. What wouldst thou now?
	If thou dar'st tempt me further, draw thy sword. [draws]
SIR TOBY	What, what? Nay, then I must have an ounce or two of this malapert blood from you. [*draws*]

Twelfth Night

DUKE	If music be the food of love, play on,
	Give me excess of it, that, surfeiting,
	The appetite may sicken and so die.
	That strain again! It had a dying fall;
	O, it came o'er my ear like the sweet sound
	That breathes upon a bank of violets,
	Stealing and giving odour! Enough, no more;
	'Tis not so sweet now as it was before.
	O spirit of love, how quick and fresh art thou!
	That, notwithstanding thy capacity
	Receiveth as the sea, nought enters there,
	Of what validity and pitch soe'er,
	But falls into abatement and low price
	Even in a minute. So full of shapes is fancy,
	That it alone is high fantastical.
CURIO	Will you go hunt, my lord?
DUKE	What, Curio?
CURIO	The hart.
DUKE	Why, so I do, the noblest that I have.
	O, when mine eyes did see Olivia first,
	Methought she purg'd the air of pestilence!
	That instant was I turn'd into a hart,
	And my desires, like fell and cruel hounds,
	E'er since pursue me.

ACT 1, SCENE 1

The Winter's Tale

HERMIONE   Since what I am to say must be but that
Which contradicts my accusation, and
The testimony on my part no other
But what comes from myself, it shall scarce boot me
To say 'Not guilty.' Mine integrity
Being counted falsehood shall, as I express it,
Be so receiv'd. But thus – if pow'rs divine
Behold our human actions, as they do,
I doubt not then but innocence shall make
False accusation blush, and tyranny
Tremble at patience.

ACT 3, SCENE 2

King Henry VI

WINCHESTER Com'st thou with deep premeditated lines,

With written pamphlets studiously devis'd?

Humphrey of Gloucester, if thou canst accuse

Or aught intend'st to lay unto my charge,

Do it without invention, suddenly;

I with sudden and extemporal speech

Purpose to answer what thou canst object.

GLOUCESTER Presumptuous priest, this place commands my patience,

Or thou shouldst find thou hast dishonour'd me.

Think not, although in writing I preferr'd

The manner of thy vile outrageous crimes,

That therefore I have forg'd, or am not able

Verbatim to rehearse the method of my pen.

No, prelate; such is thy audacious wickedness,

Thy lewd, pestiferous, and dissentious pranks,

As very infants prattle of thy pride.

Thou art a most pernicious usurer;

Froward by nature, enemy to peace;

Lascivious, wanton, more than well beseems

A man of thy profession and degree;

And for thy treachery, what's more manifest

In that thou laid'st a trap to take my life,

As well at London Bridge as at the Tower?

ACT 3, SCENE 1

Cymbeline

IMOGEN   O dissembling courtesy! How fine this tyrant

Can tickle where she wounds! My dearest husband,

I something fear my father's wrath, but nothing-

Always reserv'd my holy duty- what

His rage can do on me. You must be gone;

And I shall here abide the hourly shot

Of angry eyes, not comforted to live

But that there is this jewel in the world

That I may see again.

POSTHUMUS   My queen! my mistress!

O lady, weep no more, lest I give cause

To be suspected of more tenderness

Than doth become a man. I will remain

The loyal'st husband that did e'er plight troth;

My residence in Rome at one Philario's,

Who to my father was a friend, to me

Known but by letter; thither write, my queen,

And with mine eyes I'll drink the words you send,

Though ink be made of gall.

ACT 1, SCENE 1

As You Like It

ORLANDO	Pray thee, marry us.
CELIA	I cannot say the words.
ROSALIND	You must begin 'Will you, Orlando' –
CELIA	Go to. Will you, Orlando, have to wife this Rosalind?
ORLANDO	I will.
ROSALIND	Ay, but when?
ORLANDO	Why, now; as fast as she can marry us.
ROSALIND	Then you must say 'I take thee, Rosalind, for wife.'
ORLANDO	I take thee, Rosalind, for wife.
ROSALIND	I might ask you for your commission; but – I do take thee, Orlando, for my husband. There's a girl goes before the priest; and, certainly, a woman's thought runs before her actions.
ORLANDO	So do all thoughts; they are wing'd.
ROSALIND	Now tell me how long you would have her, after you have possess'd her.
ORLANDO	For ever and a day.
ROSALIND	Say 'a day' without the 'ever.' No, no, Orlando; men are April when they woo, December when they wed: maids are May when they are maids, but the sky changes when they are wives. I will be more jealous of thee than a Barbary cock-pigeon over his hen, more clamorous than a parrot against rain, more new-fangled than an ape, more giddy in my desires than a monkey. I will weep for nothing, like Diana in the fountain, and I will do that when you are dispos'd to be merry; I will laugh like a hyen, and that when thou are inclin'd to sleep.

ACT 4, SCENE 1

William Shakespeare
1564–1616

Why not use these pages to practice drawing your favourite Shakespeare characters?